Fun for ALL!™

Just For Boys

Search & Find®

by Tony and Tony Tallarico

3535 West Peterson Ave.
Chicago, IL 60659

Printed in China
081302002GD

Visit us at* www.kidsbooks.com/answers *for the answers.

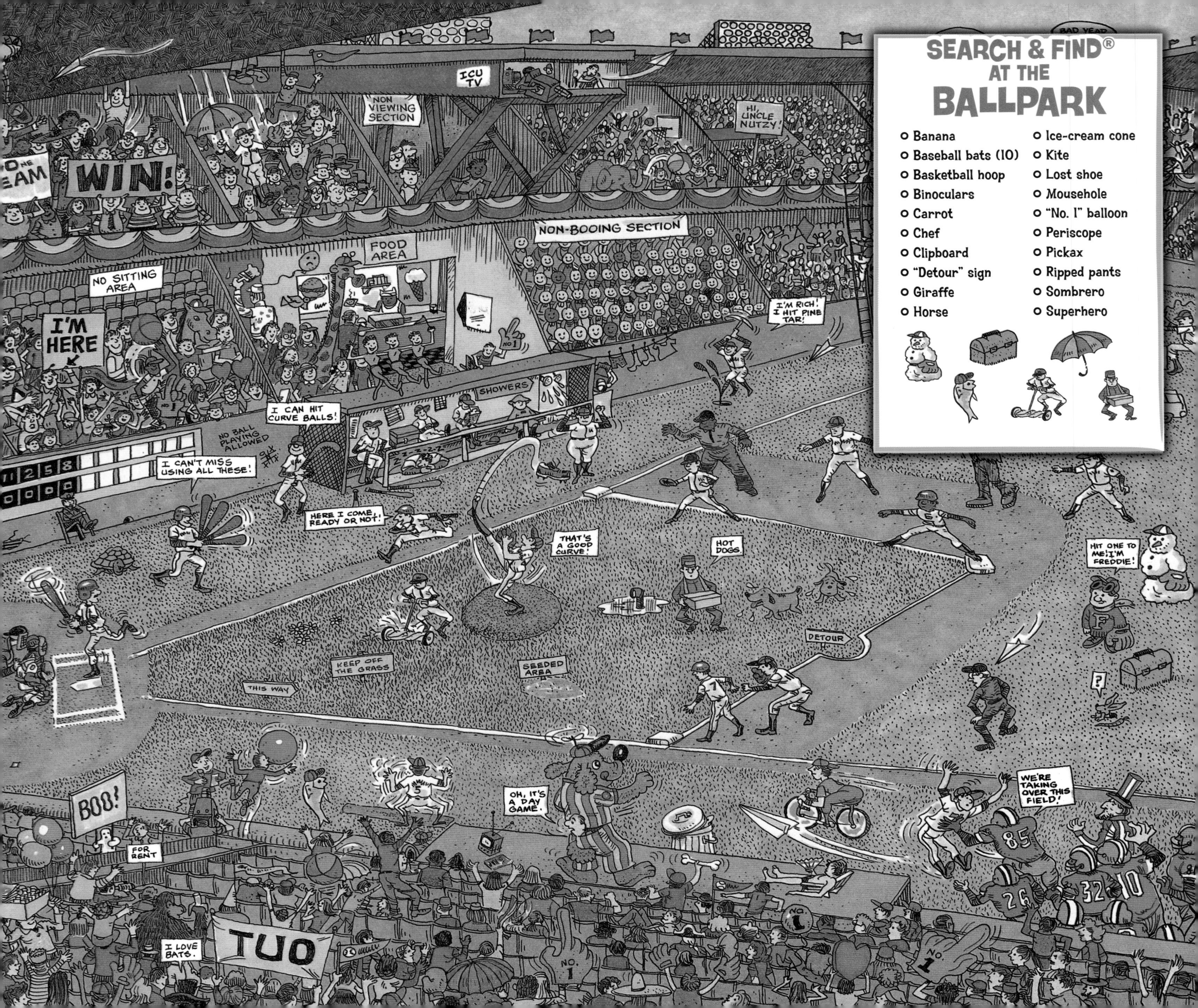
SEARCH & FIND®
AT THE
BALLPARK
Banana
Baseball bats (10)
Basketball hoop
Binoculars
Carrot
Chef
Clipboard
"Detour" sign
Giraffe
Horse
Ice-cream cone
Kite
Lost shoe
Mousehole
"No. 1" balloon
Periscope
Pickax
Ripped pants
Sombrero
Superhero
ICU TV
NON VIEWING SECTION
HI, UNCLE NUTZY!
WIN!
NON-BOOING SECTION
FOOD AREA
NO SITTING AREA
I'M HERE
I'M RICH! I HIT PINE TAR!
SHOWERS
I CAN HIT CURVE BALLS!
NO BALL PLAYING ALLOWED
I CAN'T MISS USING ALL THESE!
HERE I COME, READY OR NOT!
THAT'S A GOOD CURVE!
HOT DOGS
HIT ONE TO ME! I'M FREDDIE!
DETOUR
KEEP OFF THE GRASS
SEEDED AREA
THIS WAY
BOO!
FOR RENT
OH, IT'S A DAY GAME.
WE'RE TAKING OVER THIS FIELD!
I LOVE BATS.
TUO
NO. 1

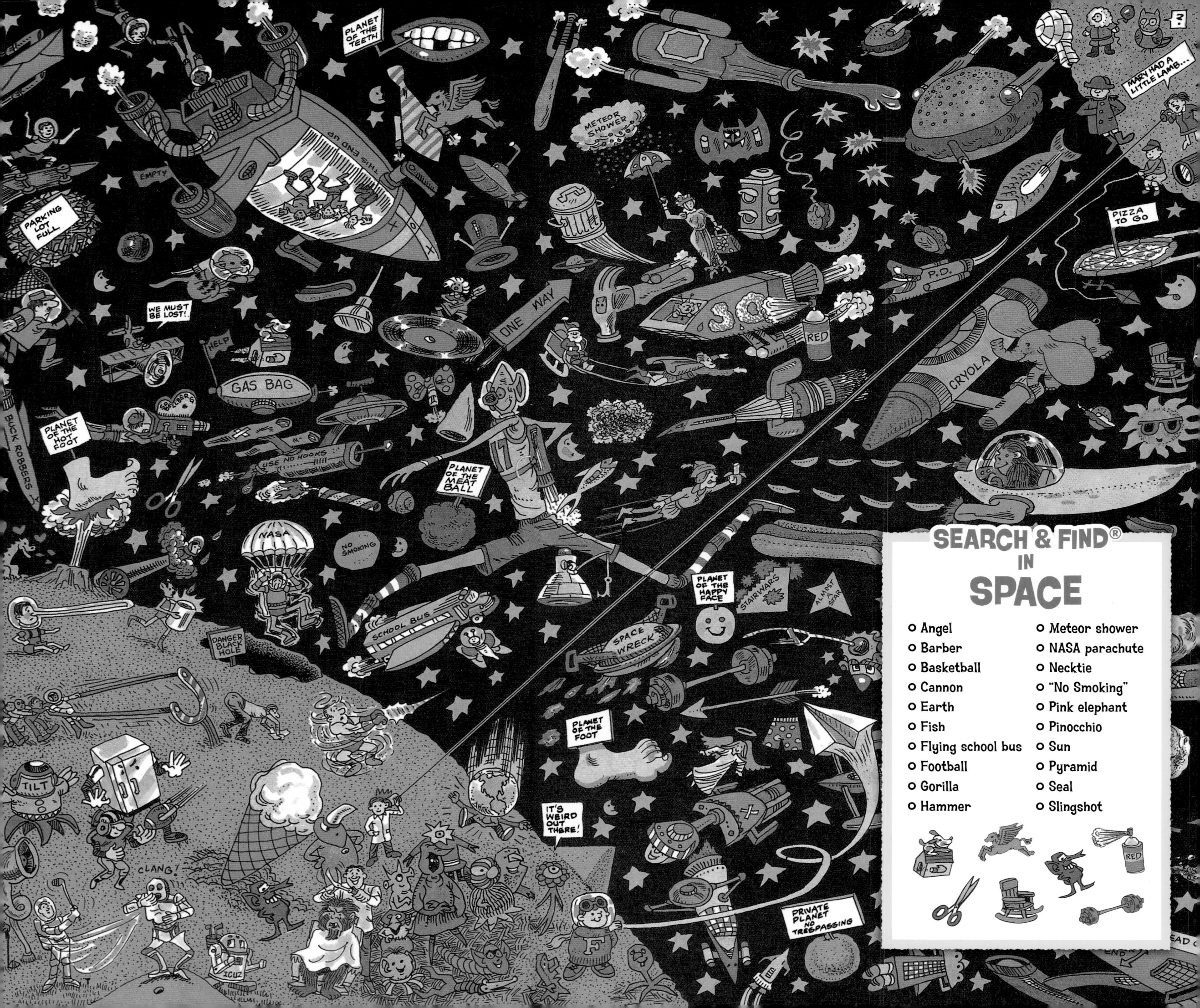

SEARCH & FIND® IN SPACE

- Angel
- Barber
- Basketball
- Cannon
- Earth
- Fish
- Flying school bus
- Football
- Gorilla
- Hammer
- Meteor shower
- NASA parachute
- Necktie
- "No Smoking"
- Pink elephant
- Pinocchio
- Sun
- Pyramid
- Seal
- Slingshot

SEARCH & FIND®
AT A
ROCK CONCERT
Alien
Artist
Barbell
Bowling ball
Clown
Doctor
Drummer
Fish tank
Flamingo
Gorilla
Guitars (3)
Hot dog stand
Knight
Lamppost
Masked man
Mummy
Pig
Rabbit
Stars (6)
Tent
I'M THE REAL CROSS WIND!
CROSSWIND BAND
ROCK IS ALIVE AND WELL!
I GO APE OVER THEIR MUSIC!
I HOPE I GET THERE BEFORE IT'S OVER!
I'M GOING TO SIGN THEM TO APPEAR IN THE BIG APPLE.
MY FAVORITE GROUP.
GO-GO-GO!
I'M GOING!
I LIKE THEM!
I WANT TO DANCE!
ARF.
PIZZA DELIVERY.
PIZZA
THIS IS BETTER THAN PICKING CORN.
OINK!
I'M THE OFFICIAL HIPPO CATCHER!
THEY CHARGED ME A TRIPLE ADMISSION FEE.
I'M THEIR MUMMY!
COME ON LISA!
WE'RE THE CALIFORNIA BEANS.
HOT DOGS
YOU ARE REALLY A BIG SPENDER.
THEY WANT TO BE LIKE US!
EVERYONE HOLD STILL SO I CAN PAINT THIS SCENE.
I JUST SAT ON A HILL OF ANTS!
HOW AM I EVER GOING TO WAKE UP EARLY TOMORROW MORNING TO CROW?
YOU CAN ORDER TWO MORE.
I'M A DOCTOR.
QUIET ZONE
WHAT IS A JOGGER DOING AT A ROCK CONCERT?
I THINK I NEED A HAIRCUT!
QUIET!
I WAS VOTED QUEEN OF THE ROCK CONCERT.
A ONE AND A TWO AND A THREE...
LOVELY MUSIC!
THAT'S THE CALIFORNIA NUT.
WHERE DO I PUT THESE RECORD ALBUMS?
HERE!
SOMEBODY GAVE ME A HOT-FOOT!
YAHOO!
SOUNDS GOOD!
NO BUS STOP
SOUNDS LOUD!
WHERE IS THE ROCK QUEEN?
THIS IS THE BEST SEAT IN THE HOUSE!
ROCK
TOO HEAVY METAL!
THIS IS THE KIND OF BAND I CAN SINK MY TEETH INTO.
ROLL
WHAT'S GOING ON HERE?
WHERE'S THE BURGER?
IS THAT THE GATOR BOWL?
COME DOWN FROM THERE!
I ♥ THAT GROUP!

SEARCH & FIND® CAT & MOUSE
FREE-FOR-ALL

- Banana peel
- Baseball
- Birdhouse
- Bone
- Broom
- Catalogue
- Catsup
- Cheese (2)
- Chimney
- Clock
- "Exit" sign
- Feather
- Fishing pole
- Karate kat
- Medal
- Mummy
- Owl
- Pickle
- Rolling pin
- Shoe for rent

SEARCH & FIND® AT THE WATER RIDE

- Apple
- Beach ball
- Bib
- Cats (2)
- Cupcake
- Elephant
- Fishing pole
- Gorilla
- Hearts (2)
- Kangaroo
- Pair of crutches
- Paper bag
- Periscope
- Peter Pan
- Pitcher
- Scuba diver
- Sea horse
- Sheep
- Snakes (2)
- Whale

SEARCH & FIND® AT THE SUPERDOG BOWL

- "107"
- Bandaged tail
- Bench
- Binoculars
- Bowl of bones
- Candy cane
- Cracked egg
- Dachshund
- Daisies (3)
- Dog pile
- Electrical outlet
- Heart-shaped turf
- "Keep off the grass"
- "Last T.D."
- "No Ball Playing"
- Paint can
- Patched pants
- Pirate hat
- Pom-poms (2)
- Referees (2)

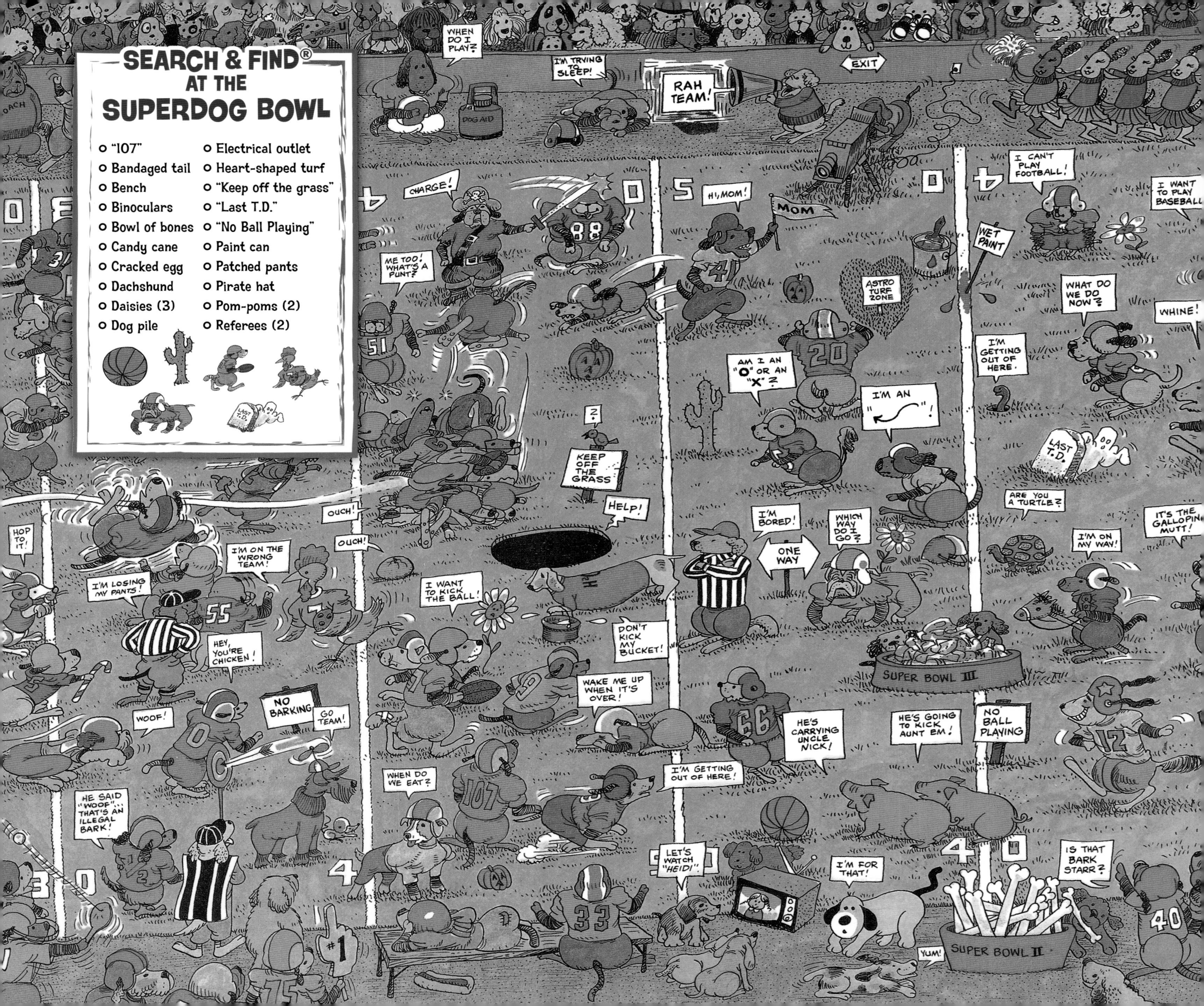

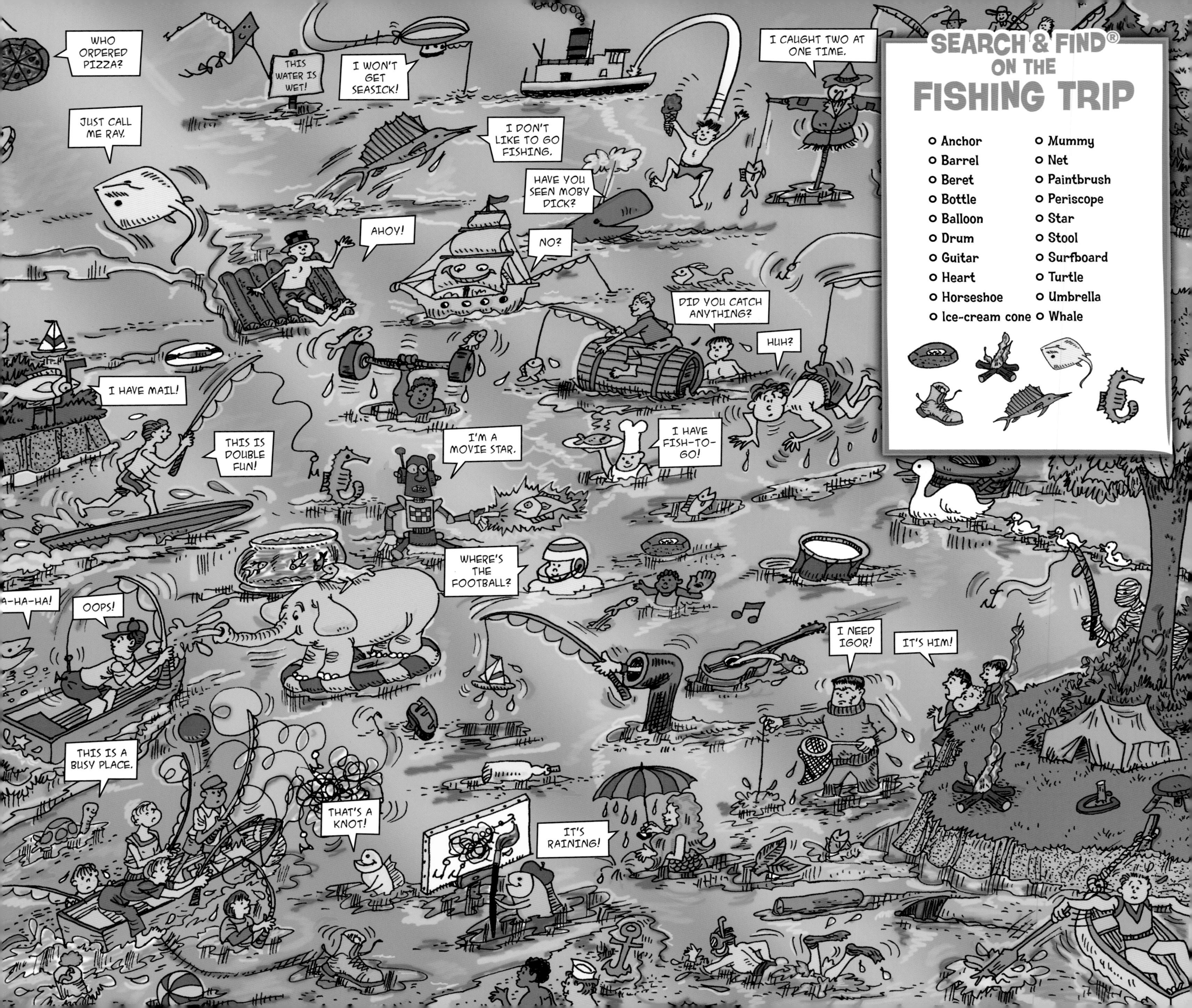

SEARCH & FIND® ON THE FISHING TRIP
Anchor
Barrel
Beret
Bottle
Balloon
Drum
Guitar
Heart
Horseshoe
Ice-cream cone
Mummy
Net
Paintbrush
Periscope
Star
Stool
Surfboard
Turtle
Umbrella
Whale
WHO ORDERED PIZZA?
THIS WATER IS WET!
I WON'T GET SEASICK!
I CAUGHT TWO AT ONE TIME.
JUST CALL ME RAY.
I DON'T LIKE TO GO FISHING.
HAVE YOU SEEN MOBY DICK?
AHOY!
NO?
DID YOU CATCH ANYTHING?
HUH?
I HAVE MAIL!
THIS IS DOUBLE FUN!
I'M A MOVIE STAR.
I HAVE FISH-TO-GO!
WHERE'S THE FOOTBALL?
A-HA-HA!
OOPS!
I NEED IGOR!
IT'S HIM!
THIS IS A BUSY PLACE.
THAT'S A KNOT!
IT'S RAINING!

SEARCH & FIND® IN THE ARCADE

- Balloon
- Baseball
- Beach ball
- Birdcage
- Black cat
- Cannon
- Darts (4)
- Dracula
- Football
- Hard hat
- Jack-o'-lantern
- Lightning
- Maze
- Mouse
- Oilcan
- Paper airplane
- Rocket
- Sailor hat
- Snakes (5)
- Umbrella

SEARCH & FIND®
AT THE
DOG OLYMPICS
Basketball
Beach ball
Bowling ball
Broom
Bucket
Dog-food bowl
Fallen skater
Golf tee
"Hi, Mom"
Home plate
Horseshoe
Ice skates (14)
Karate dog
Ping-Pong paddle
Pole-vaulter
Sleeping dogs (2)
Soccer ball
Target
Tennis racket
Yo-yo
I LOVE AMBURGERS.
HAS ANYONE SEEN HECTOR?
HAS ANYONE SEEN SNOW?
GO TEAM
HI, MOM
NO CATS ALLOWED
NO BARKING
TRAINER
I'M HECTOR. I'M A COUCH POTATO!
FETCH!
WHO'S GOT IT?
VERY THIN ICE
Z-Z-Z-Z-Z!

SEARCH & FIND® AT THE TV QUIZ SHOW

- Announcer
- "Arf TV" (3)
- Baseball cap
- Binoculars
- Candle
- Chef
- Clipboard
- Contestants (4)
- Dog food
- Drum
- Elephant
- "Exit" sign
- Flowerpot
- Game wheel
- Giraffe
- Gold bar
- Gorilla
- Headphones (5)
- Oilcan
- Sock

SEARCH & FIND® IN MONSTERVILLE

- Arrows (5)
- Broken heart
- Bucket
- Cowboy hat
- Draculas (2)
- "For Rent"
- Gorilla
- Hose
- Ice-cream cone
- Key
- Kite
- Ladder
- Mailbox
- Mousehole
- Mummy
- Number 13 (2)
- Owl
- Pyramid
- Rat
- Skeleton

SEARCH & FIND® AT HOME

- Arrow
- Baseball trophy
- Birdcage
- Bow tie
- Broken heart
- Drum
- Elephant head
- Fake teeth
- Light switch
- Mailbox
- Monster foot
- Peanuts
- Pizza
- Popcorn
- Record
- Skull
- Snake
- Top hat
- Tricycle
- Yo-yo

I'M FOR RENT.
I SMELL PIZZA.
SO DO I.
IT'S A GREAT VIEW FROM UP HERE.
FOR RENT.
WHO ORDERED THIS?
OOPS!
ANYBODY HOME?
AN APPLE A DAY...
THIS DOESN'T SMELL TOO GOOD.
WAIT FOR ME.
HI, MOM!
YOU MISSED ME.
THIS IS THE EASIER WAY DOWN.
OUCH!
LOOK OUT BELOW!
DEAR ME!
MIKE!
IKE!
I'M GETTING BETTER ALL THE TIME.
DID YOU GET LOST?
I MADE IT!
WHO HAS THE FOOTBALL?
NOT ME!
13
SEARCH & FIND®
WHILE
CAMPING
Apple
Banana peel
Beaver
Bear
Canteen
Cup
Deer
Eyeglasses
Flower
Frog
Heart
Jack-o'-lantern
Mitten
Mouse
Mushroom
Pizza delivery
Rocky Mountain sheep
Skunk
Star
Walking stick

SEARCH & FIND® AT THE DOG MALL

- Air conditioner
- "Bone on a Bun"
- Car
- Cats (2)
- Chef's hat
- Cookies (2)
- Crooked chimney
- Doghouse
- Fire hydrants (2)
- Flamingo
- Food court
- "For Rent"
- Headphones
- Hockey stick
- "Hunk" poster
- Leashes (3)
- Mug
- Pizza
- Scissors
- Spotlight

SEARCH & FIND® AT THE SILLY CIRCUS

- Banana peel
- Barrel
- Birds (3)
- Cactus
- Camel
- Cannon
- Crayon
- Firefighter
- Giraffe
- Kangaroo
- Kite
- Lightbulb
- Necktie
- Paper bag
- Party hat
- Pinocchio
- Pizza
- Police officer
- Skateboard
- Worm

SEARCH & FIND®
AT
FORT KNOCKS
Ape
Baseball cap
Bow and arrow
Candle
Cheese
Clown
Cow skull
Dog
Dragon
Footballs (2)
Lemonade stand
Lost helmets (2)
Map
Monster
Mouse
Mug
Oil can
Pie
Pot
Tank
LEMONADE 2¢
IT MUST BE A MIRAGE!
IF IT IS, IT MAKES GREAT LEMONADE.
BLAM!
DRY DESERT
MOVE IT!
I'M TAKING THE SHORT-CUT!
DID SOMETHING HAPPEN TO THE SERGEANT?
HE LOOKS OK TO ME!
TARGET RANGE
WE'LL GO THIS WAY!
WE'LL GO MY WAY!
WELCOME TO JUNGLE-LAND!
THAT WAS FUN!
SAFE?
YUM!
SLIPPERY ZONE
VERY FAST QUICK-SAND!
I'LL SOON BE A GENERAL!
YOU'RE NEXT!
THANKS
I'M WARM!
THIS LOOKS SIMPLE.
NO, THANKS.
DIG YOU MUST!
I FOUND A NEW ROUTE TO CHINA!
ZONK!
KLINK!
PUNG!
NO SITTING ZONE
CRAWL ZONE
THIS IS TOO HORRIBLE TO SHOW.
BLAP!
POW!
BASIC TRAINING
FORT KNOCKS
IS THIS THE WAY GEORGE WASHINGTON STARTED?
LET'S GO!
DOWN, BOY!
I QUIT!
HAUNTED HOUSE ZONE
IT ONLY TOOK A WEEK!
WHAT YEAR IS THIS?
CLIMB ZONE
PSYCHO ZONE
YOU MUST WATCH TV FOR TWO DAYS STRAIGHT!
VANILLA!
TUTTI-FRUTTI!
CHOCOLA
LEMO
I CAN'T STAND TV!!
ACTING LESSONS?
YOU NEED THEM!
REFRESH-MENTS
I FLUNKED!!!
TO BE OR NOT TO BE...
THAT IS THE QUESTION!
THE ANSWER IS...JOIN THE NAVY!
GHOST TOWN
OOOPS!
LOOK OUT ZONE
YIPE!
HAVE YOU SEEN MY BODY?
GUM ZONE
IT'S ALMOST OVER.
WHAT'S NEXT?
I DON'T KNOW!
I DETECT THE AROMA OF BURNING RUBBER.
LET'S GO!
IT'S THE WORST TEST OF ALL!!
OH, NO!
WILL THIS BE A GREAT ARMY FILM?
NO
MYSTERY MEALS!
CHOW?
I MUST BE SICK... THIS LOOKS GOOD!
THE END AT LAST!

SEARCH & FIND® IN THE OLD WEST

- Angel
- Apple
- Arrows (2)
- Camel
- Eight ball
- Fire hydrant
- Fishing pole
- Football
- Guitar
- Helicopter
- "ICU2"
- Monster hand
- Mouseholes (2)
- Outhouse
- Piano
- Pink elephant
- Sailboat
- Saw
- Smoke signal
- Umbrella

SEARCH & FIND® IN PREHISTORIC TIMES

- Candle
- Cherry
- Clothespin
- Dinosaur egg
- Faucet
- Hot chocolate
- Life preserver
- Necklace
- "No U Turn"
- Palm trees (3)
- Periscope
- Piggy bank
- Pizza
- Skateboard
- Spool of thread
- Stars (2)
- Sunglasses
- Tire
- Top hat
- Watch